WORDS THEIR WAY

WORD STUDY IN ACTION • SYLLABLES AND AFFIXES

W9-BMV-912

Glenview, Illinois

Boston, Massachusetts

Chandler, Arizona

Upper Saddle River, New Jersey

ALWAYS LEARNING

PEARSON

ISBN-13: 978-1-4284-3134-8
ISBN-10:   1-4284-3134-9
13 14 15 16 V011 18 17 16 15

Contents

Compound Words

bookmark	snowflake	downstairs	headfirst	lightweight
headlight	daylight	snowstorm	bookworm	downtown
cookbook	downpour	headphones	flashlight	snowplow
countdown	scrapbook	snowball	headstrong	sunlight

Sort 1: Compound Words (1)

snowman					
headline					
downhill					
lighthouse					
bookcase					

Choose words from the box to make new words. Write the words and the compound words on the lines. Draw a picture to illustrate each compound word.

light	house	sun	book	snow
worm	cook	head	phones	man

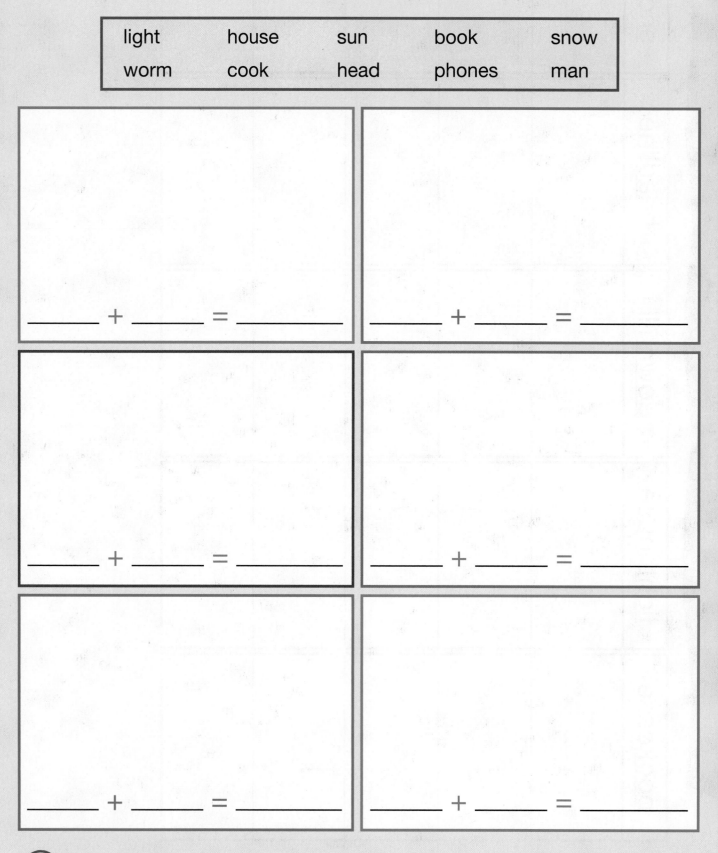

_____ + _____ = _____

_____ + _____ = _____

_____ + _____ = _____

_____ + _____ = _____

_____ + _____ = _____

_____ + _____ = _____

nothing	sometime	outfit	somehow	anything
herself	myself	somewhere	themselves	beside
sideways	itself	outside	yourself	someone
	something	throughout	outfield	checkout

Sort 2: More Compound Words (5)

inside					

without					

everything					

himself					

somebody					

Sort 2: More Compound Words (7)

Choose words from the box to make new words. On the lines, write the two words that make up the compound word and the compound word itself. You may use each word more than once.

any	them	selves	some	thing	be	your	through	no	one	out	side	time
her	check	in	my	self	ways	how	where	it	body	him	every	with

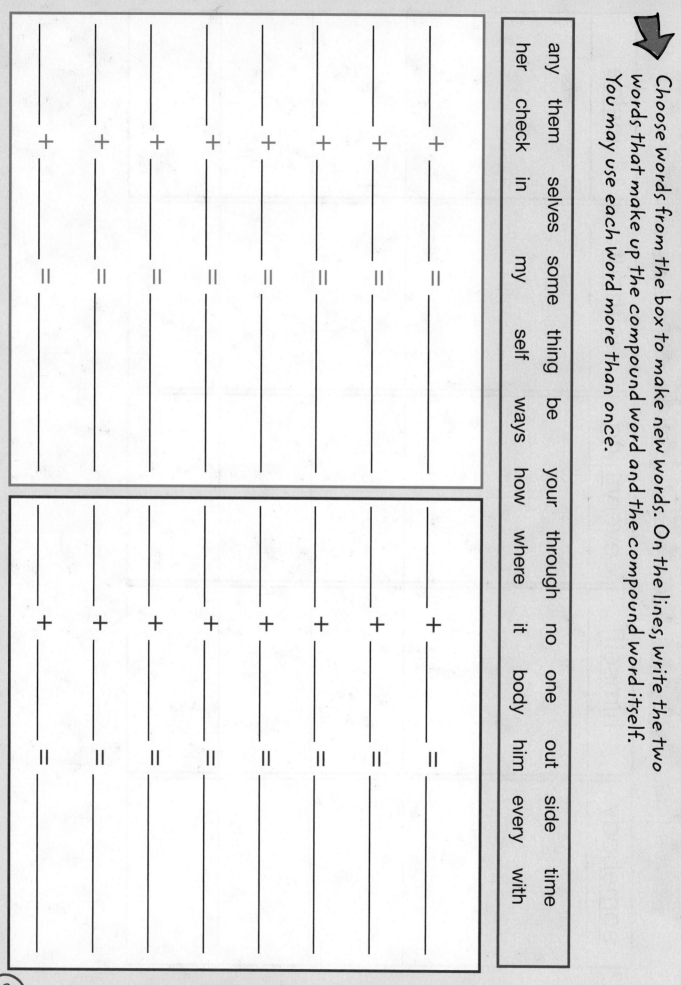

add -s	add -es	add -es	add -es	add -es
gloves	-s messes	-x foxes	-sh brushes	-ch benches
splashes	speeches	wishes	buses	taxes
crashes	churches	mixes	horses	scratches
lunches	kisses	eyelashes	peaches	voices
ashes	places	branches	changes	leashes

Plural Endings -es, -s

add -s						
gloves						

add -es						
-s messes						

add -es						
-x foxes						

add -es						
-sh brushes						

add -es						
-ch benches						

Sort 3: Plural Endings -es, -s

Make each of the following singular words plural by adding -s or -es. Write the words on the lines.

singular	plural	singular	plural
wish	_____	place	_____
kiss	_____	splash	_____
voice	_____	lunch	_____
speech	_____	change	_____
eyelash	_____	crash	_____
bus	_____	branch	_____
scratch	_____	mix	_____
horse	_____	ash	_____
peach	_____	church	_____
tax	_____	leash	_____

Unusual Plurals

goose	knife	life	leaf
knives	mouse	women	deer
mice	geese	teeth	wolves
leaves	tooth	woman	loaf
wolf	sheep	loaves	lives

no change					

vowel change					
feet					
foot					

-f or -fe to -ves					
wives					
wife					

Underline the word in each sentence that means more than one. Then write the singular form of the word on the line.

Devon thinks his cat will have nine lives. _____

Look at the geese flying through the air. _____

The kitchen knives are kept on the counter. _____

Ella often sees deer in her backyard. _____

Mia makes loaves of bread each week. _____

There were mice on the farm. _____

At night I hear wolves howling. _____

There are many women at the store. _____

Raj petted the sheep at the zoo. _____

My mother brushes her teeth after she eats. _____

The restaurant had a party for the wives. _____

Lily dipped her feet in the pool. _____

 Sort 4: Unusual Plurals

Adding -ing to Words With VC and VCC Patterns

rest	yell	run	swim
standing	jump	sit	passing
pick	put	yelling	swimming
putting	pass	stand	running
picking	jumping	resting	sitting

Sort 5: Adding -ing to Words With VC and VCC Patterns

VC base word	double + -ing	VCC base word	+ -ing
get	getting	ask	asking

Sort 5: Adding -ing to Words With VC and VCC Patterns

(19)

Complete each sentence by adding the ending -ing to the word in parentheses. Write the word on the line.

My neighbor is _____ flowers from his garden. (pick)

Rosa is _____ in a race this weekend. (run)

My mother and I like _____ together on the sofa. (rest)

Luke is _____ the ball to his teammate. (pass)

Jamal likes _____ on the park bench. (sit)

Kyle thinks _____ rope is fun. (jump)

The librarian is _____ away the returned books. (put)

Ling enjoys _____ each day after school. (swim)

Our teacher doesn't like _____ in the classroom. (yell)

Pablo gets bored _____ around. (stand)

The weather is _____ better. (get)

Sarah can't go without first _____ her parents. (ask)

Sort 5: Adding -ing to Words With VC and VCC Patterns

VCe base word + -ing	VVC base word	VCe base word e-drop + -ing	VCe base word
sneaking	**sneak**	**icing**	**ice**
eating	tune	score	blame
ride	rain	clean	use
drive	load	driving	raining
using	read	blaming	cleaning
loading	eat	riding	scoring
		reading	tuning

Sort 6: Adding -ing to Words With VCe and VVC Patterns

+ -ing
sneaking

VVC base word
sneak

e-drop + -ing
icing

VCe base word
ice

Sort 6: Adding -ing to Words With VCe and VVC Patterns

23

Make new words by adding the ending -ing to the following base words. Write the new words on the lines. Then write a sentence containing each new word.

blame _____

clean _____

score _____

rain _____

use _____

tune _____

ride _____

load _____

drive _____

read _____

eat _____

ice _____

Sort 6: Adding -ing to Words With VCe and VVC Patterns

Review of Inflected Ending -ing

spelling	adding	moving	cutting
floating	humming	living	stopping
grinning	chewing	begging	coming
snowing	jogging	taking	talking
smiling	pushing	having	working

Sort 7: Review of Inflected Ending -ing

double + -ing	e-drop + -ing	+ -ing
setting	**hiking**	**reading**

Make new words by adding the ending -ing to the
following base words. Write the new words on the lines.

cut	_____	grin	_____
move	_____	talk	_____
add	_____	take	_____
spell	_____	jog	_____
stop	_____	snow	_____
live	_____	work	_____
hum	_____	have	_____
float	_____	push	_____
come	_____	smile	_____
beg	_____	hike	_____
chew	_____	read	_____

Adding -ed (Double/No Change)

double + -ed	+ -ed
tapped	**landed**

spoiled	slipped
tripped	mailed
guarded	sobbed
cheered	dipped
chopped	loaned
shipped	punted
pouted	
hissed	asked
jumped	chained
dripped	snapped
washed	pointed
stirred	zipped
shouted	dropped
tugged	

+ -ed

landed

double + -ed

tapped

Write on the lines words that end in -ed and match the spelling pattern.

double + -ed	+ -ed
_____	_____
_____	_____
_____	_____
_____	_____
_____	_____
_____	_____
_____	_____
_____	_____
_____	_____
_____	_____
_____	_____

double + -ed	e-drop + -ed	+ -ed
stopped	**smiled**	**fished**
rocked	roared	traded
wagged	graded	clipped
baked	stamped	wasted
tasted	bailed	knitted
farmed	started	knotted
scored	rubbed	scarred
stared	handed	waved
skated	marked	whizzed

double + -ed	e-drop + -ed	+ -ed
stopped	**smiled**	**fished**

Make new words by adding the ending -ed to the base words. Write the new words on the lines. Then write a sentence containing each new word.

roar _____

bake _____

start _____

stop _____

grade _____

farm _____

fish _____

clip _____

smile _____

knot _____

wave _____

hand _____

 Sort 9: Adding -ed (Double/e-Drop/No Change)

Adding -ed to Words With VC, VCe, VVC, and VCC Patterns

wanted	waited	saved	mixed	planned
nodded	closed	helped	grabbed	seemed
shouted	hunted	stepped	liked	started
named	called	lived	dropped	passed

Sort 10: Adding -ed to Words With VC, VCe, VVC, and VCC Patterns

VC	VCe	VVC	VCC	Oddball
hopped	hoped	joined	acted	

Make new words by adding the ending -ed to the following base words. Write the new words on the lines.

plan _____   step _____

mix _____   hunt _____

save _____   shout _____

wait _____   pass _____

want _____   drop _____

seem _____   live _____

grab _____   call _____

help _____   name _____

close _____   hop _____

nod _____   hope _____

start _____   join _____

like _____   act _____

Sort 10: Adding -ed to Words With VC, VCe, VVC, and VCC Patterns

keep	shone
threw	freeze
slide	kept
froze	drive
bleed	slid
drew	sweep
know	drove
bled	draw
shine	knew
swept	throw

present	past
sleep	**slept**

Write the irregular past-tense form of each verb on the line. Then write a sentence containing the past-tense verb.

sleep _____

keep _____

draw _____

shine _____

sweep _____

throw _____

know _____

freeze _____

drive _____

slide _____

bleed _____

dinner	pretty	diner
tiger	penny	later
paper	puppy	rabbit
even	over	kitten
hello	ruler	lesson
busy	crazy	summer
open	happy	tiny

Oddball	-VCCV-		-VCV-
	supper		super

Sort 12: Syllable Juncture in VCV and VCCV Patterns

Read each of the words in the box. Write the words in the correct column. Break the words into two syllables by drawing a line between the two syllables.

dinner	pretty	diner	tiger	penny	later
paper	rabbit	even	over	kitten	hello
lesson	busy	crazy	summer	open	happy

-VCV-	-VCCV-	Oddball
su/per	sup/per	

follow	female	matter	winter
number	final	water	problem
yellow	fever	finger	butter
bottom	member	pattern	sister
blanket	pillow	moment	chapter

Sort 13: More Syllable Junctures in VCV and VCCV Patterns

(49)

-VCV-	-VCCV- doublet	-VCCV- different	Oddball
silent	happen	basket	

Sort 13: More Syllable Junctures in VCV and VCCV Patterns (51)

Read each of the words in the box. Write the words in the correct column. Break the words into two syllables by drawing a line between the two syllables.

winter	matter	female	follow	problem	water	final	number
butter	finger	fever	yellow	sister	pattern	member	moment

-VCV-
si/lent

-VCCV- doublet
hap/pen

-VCCV- different
bas/ket

Oddball

Sort 13: More Syllable Junctures in VCV and VCCV Patterns

Open and Closed Syllables in VCV Patterns

VCV Open

tuna

primate	frigid
timid	bison
chili	tiger
siren	atom
shiver	rodent
humid	cabin

VCV Closed

menu

sofa	robot
tulip	wagon
china	edit
habit	ripen
climate	comic
rapid	palace

Sort 14: Open and Closed Syllables in VCV Patterns

VCV Open

tuna

VCV Closed

menu

Read each of the words in the box. Write the words in the correct column. Break the words into two syllables by drawing a line between the two syllables.

wagon	edit	china	frigid	atom
comic	ripen	habit	bison	rodent
robot	palace	rapid	tiger	humid
sofa	tulip	climate	cabin	shiver

VCV Closed
men/u

_____

_____

_____

_____

_____

_____

_____

_____

_____

VCV Open
tu/na

_____

_____

_____

_____

_____

_____

_____

_____

_____

Sort 14: Open and Closed Syllables in VCV Patterns

never	pilot	trainer	river
student	peanut	planet	frozen
seven	humor	finish	leader
second	sneaker	present	lazy
lemon	music	minute	easy

Sort 15: Syllable Juncture in VCV and VVCV Patterns

(57)

Syllable Juncture in VCV and VVCV Patterns

-V/CV- long	-VC/V- short	-VVCV- long
human	**wagon**	**reason**

Read each of the words in the box. Write the words in the correct column. Break the words into two syllables by drawing a line between the two syllables.

river	seven	never	sneaker	peanut	minute	finish
humor	pilot	present	planet	easy	leader	lemon
trainer	lazy	frozen	second	student	music	

-V/CV- long	-VC/V- short	-VVCV- long
hu/man	wag/on	rea/son
_____	_____	_____
_____	_____	_____
_____	_____	_____
_____	_____	_____
_____	_____	_____
_____	_____	_____
_____	_____	_____
_____	_____	_____

riot	kingdom	complete	poet
subtract	monster	area	pumpkin
cruel	English	trial	kitchen
hundred	lion	control	mushroom
children	video	inspect	diet

Sort 16: Syllable Juncture in VCCCV and VV Patterns

Syllable Juncture in VCCCV and VV Patterns

-VCC/CV-	-VC/CCV-	-VV-
athlete	**pilgrim**	**create**

Sort 16: Syllable Juncture in VCCCV and VV Patterns   63

Read each of the words in the box. Write the words in the correct column. Break the words into two syllables by drawing a line between the two syllables.

poet	complete	riot	kingdom	pumpkin	subtract	monster
area	kitchen	trial	English	cruel	mushroom	control
lion	hundred	diet	inspect	video	children	

-VCC/CV-	-VC/CCV-	-VV-
ath/lete	pil/grim	cre/ate
_____	_____	_____
_____	_____	_____
_____	_____	_____
_____	_____	_____
_____	_____	_____
_____	_____	_____
_____	_____	_____

 Sort 16: Syllable Junction in VCCCV and VV Patterns

plotting	meeting	quoted
waited	faded	spelling
writing	nodded	shouting
acted	floated	skated
wanted	saving	standing
needed	hunted	taking
getting	using	leaking

-VCV-	-VCCV-	-VVCV-
hoping	**hopping**	**cleaning**

Read each of the words in the box. Write the words in the correct column. Break the words into two syllables by drawing a line between the two syllables.

plotting	meeting	quoted	waited	faded	spelling	writing
nodded	shouting	acted	floated	skated	wanted	saving
standing	needed	hunted	taking	getting	using	leaking

-VCV-	-VCCV-	-VVCV-
hop/ing	hop/ping	clean/ing
_____	_____	_____
_____	_____	_____
_____	_____	_____
_____	_____	_____
_____	_____	_____
_____	_____	_____
_____	_____	_____

Sort 17: Open and Closed Syllables and Inflected Endings

monkeys	babies	ponies
stories	alleys	parties
valleys	trays	ladies
fireflies	boys	toys
donkeys	candies	duties
berries	journeys	families

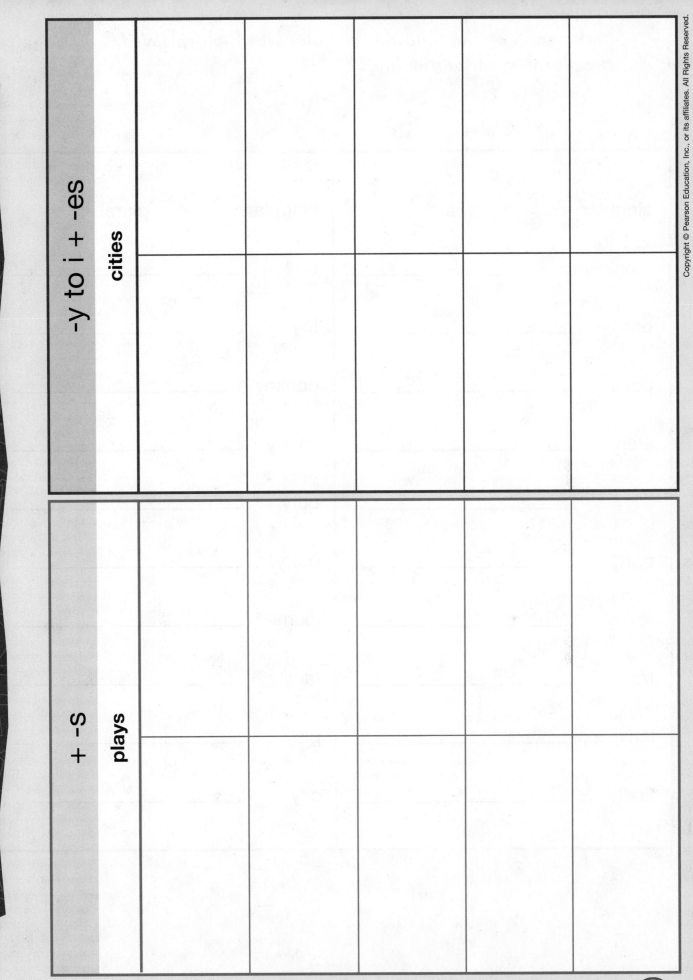

-y to i + -es					
cities					

+ -s					
plays					

Make each of the following singular words plural. Write the plural words on the lines.

singular	plural	singular	plural
monkey	_____	boy	_____
baby	_____	toy	_____
pony	_____	donkey	_____
story	_____	candy	_____
alley	_____	duty	_____
party	_____	berry	_____
valley	_____	journey	_____
tray	_____	family	_____
lady	_____	play	_____
firefly	_____	city	_____

+ -ing	+ -s	+ -ed
crying	**cries**	**cried**
replying	copying	carrying
studying	stays	hurried
replied	enjoying	copied
studies	replies	carries
enjoys	stayed	hurries
staying	studied	copies
carried	enjoyed	hurrying

Adding Inflected Endings -s, -ed, and **-ing** to Words With Final **-y**

+ -ing	+ -s	+ -ed
crying	**cries**	**cried**

	-ing	-s or + -es	-ed
reply			
copy			
enjoy			
hurry			
stay			
study			
carry			
cry			

Sort 19: Adding Inflected Endings -s, -ed, and -ing to Words With Final -y

complain	painter	decay
mistake	crayon	parade
chocolate	mayor	maybe
escape	bracelet	amaze
pavement	basement	explain
railroad	raisin	today
remain	payment	obey

Oddball

ā in 2nd Syllable

awake

ā in 1st Syllable

rainbow

Read each of the long a words in the box. Write the words in the column that shows the vowel pattern they contain. Draw a line between the two syllables. Then underline the accented syllable.

complain	painter	decay	mistake	crayon
parade	railroad	mayor	maybe	escape
bracelet	amaze	pavement	basement	explain

āi	ā_e	āy
rain/bow	a/wake	pay/ment
_____	_____	_____
_____	_____	_____
_____	_____	_____
_____	_____	_____
_____	_____	_____
_____	_____	_____

delight	ninety	surprise
machine	decide	higher
advice	brightly	survive
forgive	driveway	combine
slightly	arrive	lightning
provide	sidewalk	favorite
invite	highway	describe

Oddball	ī in 2nd syllable		ī in 1st syllable	
	polite		**frighten**	

Read each of the long i words in the box. Write the words in the column that shows the vowel pattern they contain. Draw a line between the two syllables. Then underline the accented syllable.

delight	ninety	surprise	machine	decide	higher	advice
brightly	survive	forgive	driveway	combine	slightly	arrive
lightning	provide	sidewalk	favorite	invite	highway	describe

īgh	ī_e	Oddball
fright/en	po/lite	

explode	hostess	suppose
lonely	compose	owner
bureau	lower	decode
lonesome	remote	loafer
alone	closely	Europe
soapy	approach	poster
awoke	postage	erode

Oddball	ō in 2nd syllable		ō in 1st syllable
	below		**toaster**

Read each of the long *o* words in the box. Write the words in the column that shows the vowel pattern they contain. Draw a line between the two syllables. Then underline the accented syllable.

hostess	suppose	lonely	compose	owner	closely
decode	lower	remote	loafer	alone	erode
soapy	approach	poster	awoke	postage	

ōa	ō_e	ōCC or ōw
toas/ter	ex/plode	be/low

ū in 1st syllable	ū in 2nd syllable	Oddball
rooster	**include**	
reduce	balloon	useful
cartoon	doodle	Tuesday
moody	refuse	raccoon
toothache	excuse	noodle
beauty	shampoo	pollute
conclude	scooter	confuse
cocoon	cougar	amuse

Oddball						

ū in 2nd syllable

include						

ū in 1st syllable

rooster						

Sort 23: Long u Patterns in Accented Syllables (91)

Read each of the long u words in the box. Write the words in the column that shows the vowel pattern they contain. Draw a line between the two syllables. Then underline the accented syllable.

amuse	Tuesday	raccoon	useful	pollute	moody
confuse	doodle	reduce	toothache	balloon	scooter
shampoo	beauty	cartoon	cougar	conclude	noodle

ōo	ū_e	Oddball
roos/ter	in/clude	

Sort 23: Long u Patterns in Accented Syllables

ē in 1ˢᵗ syllable	ĕ in 1ˢᵗ syllable	ē in 2ⁿᵈ syllable
needle	**feather**	**succeed**
leather	increase	season
compete	reader	heavy
defeat	pleasant	feature
sweater	freedom	indeed
meaning	steady	extreme
fifteen	eastern	repeat
thirteen	healthy	

ē in 1st syllable	ĕ in 1st syllable	ē in 2nd syllable
needle	**feather**	**succeed**

Read each of the words in the box. Write the words in the column that shows the vowel pattern and sound they contain. Draw a line between the two syllables. Then underline the accented syllable.

leather	increase	sweater	compete	reader	heavy	defeat
pleasant	feature	freedom	indeed	meaning	steady	thirteen
extreme	fifteen	eastern	repeat	healthy		

ēe or ē_e	ĕa	ēa
nee/dle	feath/er	sea/son

lightning	useful	invade
debate	speaker	freezer
delete	disease	flowing
crayon	define	advice
compose	decay	refrain
remote	enclose	frighten
salute	dispute	dainty
awake	polite	brightly

Long Vowel in 2nd Syllable

Long Vowel in 1st Syllable

Sort 25: Review Long Vowel Patterns in Accented Syllables

99

1. Read each phrase. Look at the word in boldface type. Draw a line between the two syllables.
2. Circle the long vowel in each boldface word.
3. Underline the accented syllable of each boldface word.

colored **crayon**	**define** the word
invade with caution	close the **freezer**
seek **advice**	shining **brightly**
delete the mistakes	**debate** the issue
don't **frighten** animals	**useful** instructions
salute the officer	**lightning** bolt
flowing river	**remote** control
chronic **disease**	guest **speaker**
dispute the charges	**enclose** the yard
use **polite** manners	sing the **refrain**
dainty flowers	**compose** a story

Accented Syllables

1st Syllable				2nd Syllable				Oddball
oi/oy		**ou/ow**		**oi/oy**		**ou/ow**		
voyage		drowsy		country		destroy		announce
moisture		coward		amount		thousand		avoid
poison		trouble		noisy		annoy		employ
allow		double		loyal		county		around
about		appoint		counter		southern		pointed

Sort 26: Ambiguous Vowels oy/oi and ou/ow in Accented Syllables

Ambiguous Vowels oy/oi and ou/ow in Accented Syllables

1st Syllable	
oi/oy	ou/ow

2nd Syllable		
oi/oy	ou/ow	Oddball

1. Write on the lines words that contain vowel patterns *oy, oi, ou,* and *ow.*
2. Circle the vowel pair within the word.
3. Choose two words and use each in a sentence. Write your sentences on the lines below.

oy **voyage**	oi **moisture**	ow **drowsy**

ou **announce**	ou **country**

1. _____

_____

2. _____

_____

Sort 26: Ambiguous Vowels *oy/oi* and *ou/ow* in Accented Syllables

Ambiguous Vowels au/aw/al in Accented Syllables

au sauce	aw awful	al also	oddball
always	author	almost	August
all right	lawyer	although	awkward
autumn	laundry	laughed	awesome
gnawed	caution	flawless	faucet
already	auction	gawking	sausage
haunted			

Sort 27: Ambiguous Vowels au/aw/al in Accented Syllables

au	aw	al	Oddball
sauce	awful	also	

1. Read each of the words in the box. Write the words in the column that shows the vowel pattern they contain.

2. Draw a line between the two syllables in each word. Underline the accented syllable of each word.

3. Choose three words and use each in a sentence. Write your sentences on the lines below.

awkward	laundry	always	gnawed	haunted	already
lawyer	gawking	almost	faucet	caution	flawless
autumn	sausage	awesome	author	although	

au sau/cer	aw aw/ful	al al/so

1. _____

_____

2. _____

_____

3. _____

_____

r-Influenced a in Accented Syllables

ar in 1st Syllable	ā in 1st Syllable	ā in 2nd Syllable	Oddball
garden	airplane	compare	
careful	beware	fairy	harvest
carpet	barely	partner	barefoot
haircut	aware	toward	declare
repair	parents	market	pardon
hardly	marble	despair	dairy

Sort 28: r-Influenced a in Accented Syllables

r-Influenced a in Accented Syllables

ar in 1st Syllable	ā in 1st Syllable	ā in 2nd Syllable	Oddball
garden	airplane	compare	

1. Write on the lines words that contain the r-influenced a in the first syllable or the second syllable.
2. Choose three words and use each in a sentence. Write your sentences on the lines below.

ar in 1st Syllable	ā in 1st Syllable	ā in 2nd Syllable
garden	airplane	compare

1. _____

_____

2. _____

_____

3. _____

_____

or in 1ˢᵗ Syllable	or in 2ⁿᵈ Syllable	Oddball
morning	**report**	
order	record	shorter
perform	forest	sorry
normal	reward	corner
ashore	forty	before
northern	explore	border
forward	corncob	chorus
ignore	adore	florist
inform		

r-Influenced o in Accented Syllables

Oddball								

or in 2nd Syllable

report							

or in 1st Syllable

morning							

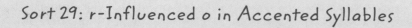

1. Write on the lines words that contain the r-influenced *o* in the first syllable or the second syllable.
2. Choose three words and use each in a sentence. Write your sentences on the lines below.

or in 1ˢᵗ Syllable	or in 2ⁿᵈ Syllable	Oddball
morning	report	

1. _____

_____

2. _____

_____

3. _____

_____

wardrobe	worse	waffle
warning	world	wander
warden	worry	squat
warrior	worthy	squash
quarter	worship	squabble
quarrel	worthwhile	squad
swarm	dwarf	backward

Words With w or /w/ Before the Vowel

/war/	/wor/	/wa/
warmth	worker	watch

1. Write on the lines words that contain w or the /w/ sound before the vowel.
2. Choose three words and use each in a sentence. Write your sentences on the lines below.

/war/	/wor/	/wa/
warmth	worker	watch

1. _____

_____

2. _____

_____

3. _____

_____

 Sort 30: Words With w or /w/ Before the Vowel

person	firmly	purpose
spirit	perfect	dirty
further	merry	certain
birthday	hurry	mermaid
thirsty	turtle	perhaps
birdbath	furnish	service
during	Thursday	circle

er	ir	ur	Oddball
nervous	**thirty**	**sturdy**	

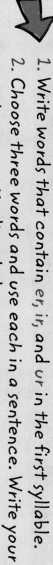

1. Write words that contain er, ir, and ur in the first syllable.
2. Choose three words and use each in a sentence. Write your sentences on the lines below.

er	ir	ur	Oddball
nervous	thirty	sturdy	

1. _____

2. _____

3. _____

sermon	earthquake	teardrop
sincere	cheerful	serpent
learner	spearmint	adhere
hermit	pearly	yearbook
merely	thermos	rehearse
appear	kernel	yearning
dreary	earnest	searching

/ər/ and r-Influenced ē Spelled er, ear, ere, eer in Accented Syllables

ər

er = /ur/	ear = /ur/	
mercy	early	

r-Influenced ē

ear	ere	eer
nearby	severe	career

1. Write words that contain /ər/ and r-influenced ē on the lines.

2. Choose two words and use each in a sentence. Write your sentences on the lines below.

ə r	
er = /ur/ <u>mer</u>/cy	**ear = /ur/** <u>ear</u>/ly

r-Influenced ē		
ear <u>near</u>/ly	**ere** se/<u>vere</u>	**eer** ca/<u>reer</u>

1. _____

_____

2. _____

_____

 Sort 32: /ər/ and r-Influenced ē Spelled er, ear, ere, eer in Accented Syllables

cradle	middle	tremble
able	table	single
settle	bottle	scribble
rifle	muscle	sample
rattle	paddle	battle
bugle	bridle	handle
cable	jungle	scramble

VCle title	VCCle doublet little	VCCle simple

1. Read each sentence. Choose a word from the box that best completes the sentence and write it on the line. (Note: Not all words have to be used and each word can be used only once.)
2. Draw a line between the two syllables in each word.
3. Underline the accented syllable of each word.

scramble	battle	cable	rattle	scribble	able	rifle
handle	tremble	settle	cradle	bugle	jungle	single
table	paddle	bridle	middle	muscle	sample	bottle

1. The kayaker used her _____ to glide across the water.

2. Amin's family eats dinner at the _____ each night.

3. Megan's hands _____ when she is nervous.

4. The audience heard the _____ blare at the concert.

5. The athlete pulled a _____ while running.

6. The veterinarian used his hands to _____ the kitten.

7. Sonya ordered a _____ of water with lunch.

8. Monkeys and tigers live in the _____.

9. The rock climber used a safety _____ when climbing.

saddle	level	April
total	fragile	couple
angel	fossil	metal
special	angle	novel
evil	signal	needle
pedal	stencil	local
bundle	vowel	journal
cancel	pupil	jewel
struggle	council	

Oddball	-al	-il	-el	-le
	final	**pencil**	**model**	**cattle**

1. Write on the lines words that contain -le, -el, -il, or -al in the final syllable.
2. Underline the accented syllable of each word.

-le <u>cat</u>tle	-el <u>mod</u>el	-il <u>pen</u>cil	-al <u>fi</u>nal	Oddball

brother	doctor	dollar
favor	rather	solar
cover	flavor	mirror
motor	sugar	grammar
weather	silver	father
rumor	popular	tractor
mother	harbor	lunar
regular	cedar	after
calendar	flower	error

-er	-ar	-or
spider	**collar**	**color**

1. Write on the lines words that contain -er, -ar, or -or in the final syllable.
2. Draw a line between the two syllables and underline the accented syllable in each word.
3. Choose three words and use each in a sentence. Write your sentences on the lines below.

-er	-ar	-or
<u>spi</u>/der	<u>col</u>/lar	<u>col</u>/or

1. _____

_____

2. _____

_____

3. _____

_____

dreamer	creator	later
sooner	driver	sailor
stronger	farmer	visitor
smaller	jogger	editor
fresher	writer	younger
swimmer	older	smoother
voter	director	juror
governor	shopper	brighter

Agents and Comparatives

People Who Do Things		Words to Compare
dancer	**actor**	**bigger**

1. Read each word. Make new words by adding the ending -er, -ar, or -or. (Double the final consonant and drop the e as necessary.) Write the new words on the lines.

2. Write an A above the agents and a C above the comparatives.

Agent or Comparative	Agent or Comparative
shop _____	edit _____
old _____	write _____
dream _____	strong _____
create _____	young _____
big _____	vote _____
drive _____	smooth _____
visit _____	sail _____
soon _____	farm _____
jog _____	govern _____
fresh _____	swim _____
dance _____	small _____
direct _____	act _____
bright _____	jury _____

rancher	nature	pressure
failure	senior	teacher
capture	pleasure	danger
pitcher	future	leisure
mixture	treasure	pasture
culture	posture	obscure
secure	stretcher	marcher

-cher = /chur/ catcher	-ture = /chur/ picture	-sure = /zhur/ measure	-ure = /yur/ figure	Oddball

Sort 37: Final Syllable /ər/ Spelled -cher, -ture, -sure, -ure

Write on the lines words that contain -cher, -ture, -sure, or -ure in the final syllable.

-cher = /chur/	-ture = /chur/
catcher	**picture**
_____	_____
_____	_____
_____	_____
_____	_____
_____	_____
_____	_____

-sure = /zhur/	-ure = /yur/	Oddball
measure	figure	
_____	_____	_____
_____	_____	_____
_____	_____	_____
_____	_____	_____
_____	_____	_____
_____	_____	_____

eleven	unison	captain
woman	mission	oxygen
gallon	bargain	organ
heaven	ribbon	fountain
orphan	chosen	apron
curtain	slogan	abdomen
bacon	children	certain
urban	pardon	villain

-en	-on	-an	-ain	Oddball
broken	dragon	human	mountain	

Sort 38: Unaccented Final Syllable /ən/ Spelled -en, -on, -an, -ain

(151)

1. Read the beginning of each word. Choose the final syllable
   -en, -on, -an, or -ain that best completes the word.
2. Write the new word on the line and read it aloud.
3. Choose three words and use each in a sentence. Write your sentences
   on the lines below.

elev___	_____	fount___	_____
suburb___	_____	heav___	_____
capt___	_____	ribb___	_____
wom___	_____	chos___	_____
oxyg___	_____	orph___	_____
missi___	_____	apr___	_____
gall___	_____	curt___	_____
barg___	_____	slog___	_____
org___	_____	childr___	_____
abdom___	_____	bac___	_____
urb___	_____	pard___	_____
unis___	_____	cert___	_____
vill___	_____		

1. _____

_____

2. _____

_____

3. _____

_____

Sort 38: Unaccented Final Syllable /ən/ Spelled -en, -on, -an, -ain

another	degree	believe
divide	awhile	depend
between	direct	among
desire	beneath	upon
aboard	develop	because
against	defend	begun
afraid	aloud	astonish
behavior	agenda	decision
beforehand	delete	

Oddball	be-	de-	a-
	beyond	**debate**	**again**

Sort 39: Unaccented Initial Syllables a-, de-, be-

1. Read the ending of each word. Choose the initial syllable a-, de-, or be- that best completes the word.
2. Write the new word on the line and read it aloud.
3. Choose two words and use each in a sentence. Write your sentences on the lines below.

___nother _____   ___neath _____

___gree _____   ___board _____

___lieve _____   ___velop _____

___stonish _____   ___cause _____

___while _____   ___gainst _____

___yond _____   ___fend _____

___pend _____   ___gun _____

___tween _____   ___bate _____

___mong _____   ___fraid _____

___sire _____   ___loud _____

___gain _____   ___lete _____

___genda _____   ___havior _____

___forehand _____   ___cision _____

1. _____

_____

2. _____

_____

Sort 39: Unaccented Initial Syllables a-, de-, be-

circle	gymnast	common
gossip	central	giraffe
camel	golden	century
genius	college	garage
cyclist	general	custom
gutter	cider	gingerbread
collect	cereal	govern
gurgle	cavern	giant

Hard g	Hard c	Soft g	Soft c
gather	correct	gentle	cement

1. Read each sentence. Choose a word from the box that best completes the sentence and write it on the line. (Note: Not all words will be used and each word can be used only once.)
2. Underline the vowel that follows the c or g.
3. Circle the word if it has a soft c or g.

circle	central	century	cyclist	cider	gather
gymnast	giraffe	genius	govern	giant	correct
common	cavern	college	custom	collect	cement
gossip	golden	garage	gutter	cereal	gentle

1. The book club will _____ weekly.

2. The _____ gained speed on the downhill slope.

3. Aida plans to major in biology at _____.

4. The teacher outlined the _____ concept of the project.

5. The craftsman made a _____ desk.

6. My cousin is training to become a _____.

7. Apple _____ was served at the harvest party.

8. Some of the leaves had changed to a _____ color.

9. Malik volunteered to _____ the problem.

10. There was a _____ breeze near the ocean.

11. The class measured the diameter of the _____.

12. Cheryl stores her athletic equipment in the _____.

13. We explored the underground _____.

14. Our teacher asked for a volunteer to _____ our reports.

15. My teacher discourages _____ at school.

Sort 40: Initial Hard and Soft c and g

garbage	police	manage	fidget
princess	gadget	sentence	actress
luggage	address	surgeon	distance
science	package	compass	office
courage	message	practice	village
express	possess	challenge	arrange

Sort 41: Final -s and Soft c and g

-age = /ij/ bandage								

ge = /j/ budget								

-ss = /s/ recess								

-ce = /s/ notice								

Write on the lines words that contain -ce, -ss, ge, or -age in the final syllable.

-ce = /s/ notice	-ss = /s/ recess	-ge = /j/ budget	-age = /ij/ bandage

vague	guard	language
gauge	shrug	league
guitar	zigzag	guide
fatigue	iceberg	argue
strong	guilty	guest
dialogue	guidance	plague
intrigue	catalog	penguin

Oddball	-g ladybug	-gue vogue	gu- guess

Read each sentence. Choose a word from the box that best completes the sentences and write it on the line. (Note: Not all words will be used and each word can be used only once.)

guard	guitar	guide	guilty	guidance
vague	league	fatigue	strong	plague
zigzag	shrug	iceberg	guest	intrigue
gauge	language	argue	dialogue	catalog

1. The musician played a _____ while she sang.

2. My grandfather has a _____ memory of his childhood.

3. Claire picked out a new outfit from the _____.

4. The coach encouraged the players to _____ off their loss.

5. Jin planned his class schedule with some _____ from his advisor.

6. The smell of the fresh flowers was _____.

7. The bowling _____ competes on Saturday mornings.

8. Tourists followed a tour _____ around the city.

9. My grandmother speaks more than one _____.

10. The actor memorized his _____ for the movie.

11. After the marathon, Marcella was overcome with _____.

12. The hikers followed the _____ path down the mountain.

13. We went to the auditorium to hear the _____ speaker.

14. The penguins gathered on the _____.

15. A light went on when the gas _____ was near empty.

quick	pocket	traffic
index	stomach	hammock
nickel	topic	complex
attack	pickle	picnic
buckle	metric	ticket
electric	plastic	perplex
shoebox	jacket	racetrack
rocket	fabric	unlock
struck	specific	

-ck	ck	-ic	-x	Oddball
shock	chicken	magic	relax	

Write on the lines words that contain the /k/ sound spelled as ck, -ic, or -x.

-ck shock	ck chicken	-ic magic
_____	_____	_____
_____	_____	_____
_____	_____	_____
_____	_____	_____
_____	_____	_____
_____	_____	_____
_____	_____	_____

-x relax	Oddball
_____	_____
_____	_____
_____	_____
_____	_____
_____	_____
_____	_____
_____	_____

Sort 43: /k/ Spelled ck, -ic, -x

squirrel	racquet	frequent	quality
equator	squirming	mosquito	equipment
quotation	banquet	quadrant	conquer
queasy	liquid	quizzes	inquire
qualify	request	sequel	sequence
		critique	technique

1st Syllable	2nd Syllable	qu = /k/
question	equal	antique

1. Read each sentence. Choose a word from the box that best completes the sentence and write it on the line. (Note: Not all words will be used and each word can be used only once.)
2. Draw a line between the two syllables in each word.

request	quality	sequel	conquer	inquire	queasy
question	frequent	mosquito	equator	quizzes	sequence
equal	racquet	squirming	banquet	liquid	qualify
antique	equipment	squirrel	quotation	technique	quadrant

1. The tennis player prepared to serve by raising his _____.

2. Snowstorms in the northeast are _____ in winter.

3. Shayna located the _____ on the globe.

4. My grandmother has several _____ quilts in her home.

5. Some of the kids felt _____ after the roller-coaster ride.

6. My sister hopes to _____ for the race.

7. The coach spoke at the awards _____.

8. The _____ buried the acorns in the yard.

9. Luckily, I returned from the forest with no _____ bites.

10. My backpack is made of _____ material.

11. The team hoped to _____ its opponent.

12. The hiker was responsible for carrying her _____ on the expedition.

13. Raj called the radio station with his music _____.

14. Our English teacher likes to give surprise _____.

15. Vonelle could not wait to read the _____ to the novel.

fasten	resign	wreckage
knowledge	honor	thought
listen	assignment	wrestle
rhyme	brought	glisten
answer	rhythm	bought
khaki	though	doorknob
campaign	kneepad	soften
gnarl	sword	knockout

Words With Silent Consonants

Silent t castle	Silent g design	Silent w wrinkle

Silent k knuckle	Silent h honest	Silent gh through

1. Read the incomplete word. Choose the silent letter t, g, w, k, h, or letters gh that best completes the word.

2. Write the new word on the line and read it aloud.

3. Choose three words and use each in a sentence. Write your sentences on the lines below.

fas___en _____

___nowledge _____

lis___en _____

r___yme _____

ans___er _____

campai___n _____

___narl _____

k___aki _____

resi___n _____

___onor _____

assi___nment _____

brou___t _____

r___ythm _____

thou___ _____

___neepad _____

s___ord _____

___reckage _____

thou___t _____

___restle _____

glis___en _____

bou___t _____

door___nob _____

sof___en _____

___nockout _____

1. _____

_____

2. _____

_____

3. _____

_____

Sort 45: Words With Silent Consonants

physics	elephant	cough
naughty	phantom	nephew
tough	taught	photocopy
dolphin	rough	caught
photograph	trophy	laughter
fought	telephone	homophone
paragraph	phonics	height

Words With gh and ph

Silent gh	-gh = /f/	ph	ph-
daughter	enough	alphabet	phrase

1. Write words on the lines that contain ph, gh = /f/, and silent gh.
2. Choose three words and use each in a sentence. Write your sentences on the lines below.

ph- phrase	ph alphabet	-gh = /f/ enough	silent gh daughter

1. _____

2. _____

3. _____

recopy	uncle	unkind
recycle	unwrap	reptile
refill	unselfish	refinish
unbutton	unhappy	rewrite
retrace	unpack	retake
unfair	return	uneven
review	unequal	unbeaten
remodel	rescue	

Oddball					

un-					
unable					

re-					
rebuild					

1. Write the meaning of the prefix on the line next to each header.

Prefix re-: _____

Prefix un-: _____

 2. Make new words by adding the prefix re- or un- to the
following base words. Write the words on the lines.
(Note: You can add more than one prefix to some words.)

___build _____   ___button _____

___able _____   ___write _____

___copy _____   ___trace _____

___cycle _____   ___pack _____

___kind _____   ___take _____

___wrap _____   ___fair _____

___fill _____   ___turn _____

___selfish _____   ___even _____

___finish _____   ___view _____

___happy _____   ___equal _____

___model _____   ___beaten _____

dislike	mistreat	prefix
precious	disable	mismatch
premature	disobey	misplace
preteen	displace	misbehave
preview	dishonest	misjudge
preheat	disloyal	pretest
disappear	precaution	mister
miscount	distant	mistrust

Oddball	pre-	mis-	dis-
	preschool	misspell	disagree

1. Make new words by adding the prefix dis-, mis-, or pre- to the following base words. Write the words on the lines. (Note: You can add more than one prefix to some words.)

___like _____	___behave _____
___treat _____	___view _____
___fix _____	___honest _____
___able _____	___judge _____
___match _____	___heat _____
___mature _____	___loyal _____
___obey _____	___test _____
___place _____	___appear _____
___teen _____	___caution _____
___cover _____	___agree _____
___spell _____	___school _____
___count _____	___trust _____

 2. Choose three derived words and write a definition for each.

1. _____

2. _____

3. _____

extend	nonfiction	incorrect
forearm	extra	nonstop
indecent	forehead	express
nonfat	foresee	exclude
foreshadow	explode	income
foremost	expand	nonprofit
insight	explore	indoor
nonskid	inhuman	

ex-	non-	in- ("not")	fore-
exit	nonsense	incomplete	forecast

		in- ("in" or "into")	
		indent	

Sort 49: Prefixes ex-, non-, in-, fore-

1. Write the meaning of the prefix on the line next to each header.

Prefix ex-: _____

Prefix non-: _____

Prefix in-: _____

Prefix fore-: _____

2. Make new words by adding the prefix ex-, non-, in-, or fore- to the following base words or word parts. Write the words on the lines. (Note: You can add more than one prefix to some words.)

___tend _____   ___shadow _____

___fiction _____   ___plode _____

___correct _____   ___come _____

___arm _____   ___most _____

___plore _____   ___pand _____

___stop _____   ___door _____

___decent _____   ___sight _____

___head _____   ___human _____

___press _____   ___complete _____

___fat _____   ___sense _____

___see _____   ___cast _____

___clude _____   ___dent _____

___profit _____   ___skid _____

Sort 49: Prefixes ex-, non-, in-, fore-

unique	unity	biweekly	trilogy
octagon	bisect	triangle	unicorn
octopus	triple	bilingual	pentagon
unison	October	triplet	union
universe	trio	uniform	tripod

Other Number Prefix quadrangle	tri- tricycle	bi- bicycle	uni- unicycle

1. Write the meaning of the prefix on the line next to each header.

Prefix uni-: _____

Prefix bi-: _____

Prefix tri-: _____

Other Number Prefix: _____

 2. Make new words by adding the prefix uni-, bi-, tri-, or that of some other number to the following base words or word parts. Write the words on the lines. (Note: You can add more than one prefix to some words or word parts.)

___cycle _____

___rangle _____

___ty _____

___weekly _____

___logy _____

___agon _____

___corn _____

___sect _____

___angle _____

___que _____

___lingual _____

___ple _____

___opus _____

___on _____

___plet _____

___ober _____

___son _____

___pod _____

___form _____

___verse _____

clearly	quickly	easily
angrily	rainy	foggy
snowy	noisily	lazily
loudly	quietly	dimly
stormy	misty	windy
daily	cloudy	roughly
chilly	sleepily	breezy
busily	smoothly	merrily

-y	-ly	-ily
sunny	**slowly**	**happily**

1. Read each sentence. Choose a base word from the box that best completes the sentence. (Note: Not all words will be used and each word can be used only once.)

2. Add the suffix -y, -ly, or -ily to the word. (Change -y to i, drop the e, and double the final letter as necessary.) Write the adjective or adverb on the line.

rain	clear	lazy	storm	cloud	breeze	merry
quick	angry	mist	loud	rough	happy	sleepy
easy	snow	quiet	chill	wind	sun	busy
fog	dim	noisy	day	smooth	slow	

1. During _____ weather, we prepare to stay indoors.

2. The emergency vehicle moved _____ to the hospital.

3. After much practice, Dana _____ completed the equation.

4. We used a flashlight to explore the _____ lit cave.

5. My family likes to ski in a _____ location.

6. Our cat _____ moved from the floor after napping.

7. The news anchor _____ delivered his lines.

8. Greg _____ shared his good news with the class.

9. At the library, we work together _____.

10. The excited friends _____ greeted one another.

11. Flying a kite is fun to do on a _____ day.

12. Talia shielded her face from the _____ wind.

13. The parade of people passed _____ through town.

14. The hikers moved slowly up the _____ path.

15. On _____ days it's fun to look for shapes in the sky.

calmer	prettiest	dirtier
easiest	closer	crazier
coolest	calmest	hotter
fewest	closest	craziest
weaker	prettier	easier
dirtiest	fewer	hottest
cooler	weakest	lazier
funniest	laziest	funnier

-er braver	-est bravest	-ier happier	-iest happiest

1. Make new words by adding the suffix -er or -est to the following base words. (Change -y to i, drop the e, and double the final letter as necessary.) Write the words on the lines.

2. Write three new base words on the lines provided. Make new words by adding the suffix -er or -est to these words. (Change -y to i, drop the e, and double the final letter as necessary.) Write the words on the lines.

	-er	-est
funny		
lazy		
calm		
easy		
close		
pretty		
few		
crazy		
cool		
dirty		
hot		
weak		
brave		
happy		
_____		
_____		
_____		

Sort 53: Suffixes -ness, -ful, -less

thankfulness	hopeless	goodness
helplessness	happiness	faithful
peacefulness	restless	weakness
worthless	penniless	painful
plentiful	dreadful	harmless
fearless	gratefulness	awareness

colorful
thoughtfulness
illness
kindness
fearful
truthfulness

-ness	-ful	-less	Combination of Suffixes
darkness	graceful	homeless	carelessness

1. Write the meaning of the suffix on the line next to each header.

Suffix -ness: _____

Suffix -ful: _____

Suffix -less: _____

 2. Make new words by adding the suffix -ness, -ful, or -less, or a combination of these suffixes to the following base words. (Change -y to i as necessary.) Write the words on the lines.

care _____		ill _____
home _____		thought _____
dark _____		rest _____
grace _____		peace _____
good _____		kind _____
color _____		hope _____
hope _____		pain _____
thank _____		penny _____
weak _____		happy _____
faith _____		fear _____
worth _____		harm _____
help _____		plenty _____
dread _____		truth _____
aware _____		grate _____

Sort 53: Suffixes -ness, -ful, -less

cellar	weather
allowed	flour
bored	seller
whether	aloud
flower	board
vary	their
desert	principle
chews	merry
very	higher
dessert	principal
choose	marry
there	hire

Homophones

berry	bury

1. Say each word aloud. Think of a word that sounds the same but is spelled differently and has a different meaning.
2. Write a sentence that uses the new word.
3. Underline the homophone.

cellar _____

weather _____

allowed _____

flower _____

board _____

their _____

merry _____

very _____

dessert _____

principal _____

choose _____

hire _____

bury _____

desert _____

aloud _____

verb		noun	
present		**present**	
rebel	permit	record	desert
rebel	record	desert	permit
object	reject	object	subject
export	conduct	produce	subject
contract	produce	reject	conduct
		contract	export

verb	present						

noun	present						

Sort 55: Homographs (219)

Write a sentence using each word as a noun and a verb.

present _____

desert _____

record _____

permit _____

rebel _____

object _____

subject _____

reject _____

produce _____

conduct _____

export _____

contract _____

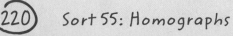